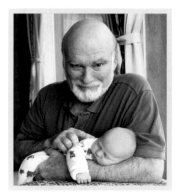

*"Early childhood is the time when we have
the greatest chance to make positive contributions
to a child's development."*

DR. ANDREW MACNAB
Pediatrician, Child Health Researcher, Distinguished Scholar

i

A B C D E F G H I J K L

A B C D E F G H I J K L

Foreword

Today's families come in many forms. This ABC book is for all parents and caregivers, and those who support them.

Social and emotional development is key to a child's health and happiness. A secure early relationship with a loving – and responsive – caregiver puts babies and toddlers on the path for lifelong mental, emotional and physical health, and lifelong learning.

Nurturing babies helps them grow to be caring, compassionate, empathetic, resilient, productive, happy and healthy adults.

Parents who nurture their babies in the ways described in this book and in the resources, are giving their child the most precious gift of all, and one that lasts a lifetime.

Videos are freely available at www.kidcarecanada.org
A QR code on each page takes you to relevant videos or websites.

"Lack of sleep can make everything seem overwhelming.

Alligator

Anxiety

Parenthood can be an emotional time. It is perfectly normal to experience some highs and lows adjusting to your role as a parent. Lack of sleep can make **everything** seem overwhelming.

Ask for help right away and connect with your health care professional if:

- you are feeling anxious or depressed for more than two weeks
- you have had thoughts of harming yourself or your baby
- you feel out of control about anything

(See resources at the back of this book)

Brain Development

Healthy brain development happens when babies feel safe. It begins before birth. When you do the following before birth you support your baby's healthy growth and brain development:

- have regular prenatal care
- take time to rest, and minimize stress when you can
- eat a variety of healthy foods
- avoid alcohol, other drugs and tobacco

Once your baby is born, nutrition, nurturing and sleep will help your baby's brain develop.

Breastfeeding is good for your baby's developing brain. It is the only food your baby needs for the first 6 months.

If you are unable to breastfeed or need to supplement your breast milk, hold your child close (skin-to-skin), look into your child's eyes when you are feeding and watch for their feeding cues.

" It is never too late to nurture a child but early nurture provides the best foundation for healthy brain development.

"Nutrition, nurturing and sleep help your baby's brain develop.

At about 6 months introduce nutritious and safe table foods. Did you know breastfeeding is beneficial for up to 2 years, and beyond?

Positive **early** experiences protect your baby throughout life!

Your baby needs a dependable relationship with at least one loving *and responsive* caregiver, especially for the first 2 years of life. Frequent eye contact, talking, listening, and playing:

> 🧸 build your baby's brain in a positive way
> 🧸 set your child up for mental, emotional and physical health
> 🧸 help your baby develop the ability to learn well,
> in and out of school

Babies cannot learn from TVs or screens that can be harmful for their development and may lead to sleep and other problems. A safe exception is video chats with an absent loving family member or friend.

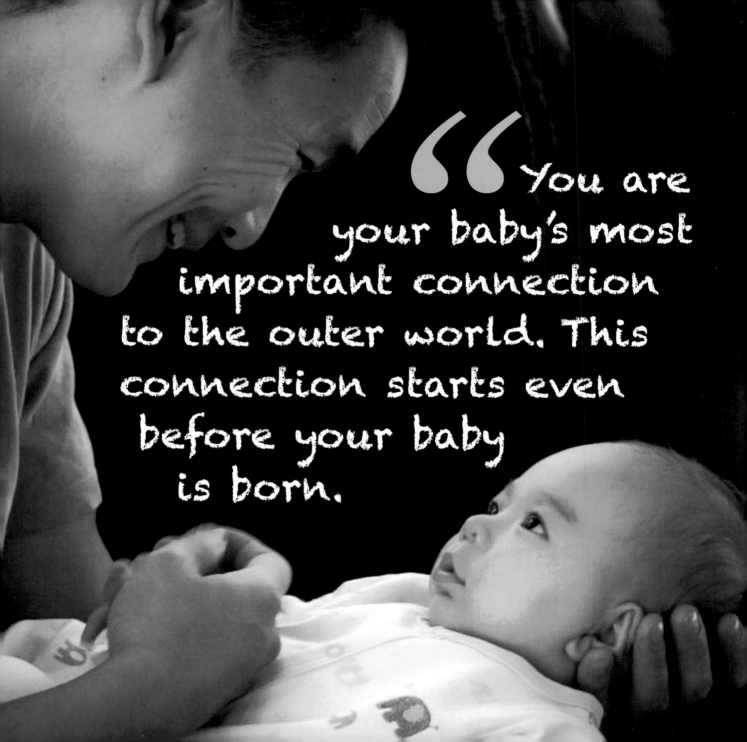

"You are your baby's most important connection to the outer world. This connection starts even before your baby is born.

Connection

cat

The connection with your baby starts before your baby is born. You can begin to sing, talk and read to your baby when your baby is in the womb.

A secure connection with you lowers your baby's stress and helps your baby thrive and grow. To build that connection, watch for your baby's cues and:

- comfort and reassure your baby when your baby seems upset
- let your baby lie on you or your partner skin-to-skin
- hold, stroke and rock your baby
- look into your baby's eyes and mirror your baby's expressions
- sing or hum to your baby
- read to your baby or tell stories pointing at pictures (you can use this book!)
- take walks with your baby – point out whatever you see, such as trees – your child will have a richer learning experience

Other ways to build the connection with your baby are:

- play, smile and laugh with your baby – your baby will eventually respond
- talk with your baby and explain what is happening
- let your baby have quiet time when they seem overstimulated

As you learn to read and respond to your baby's cues, your baby will see you as their "someone" who can meet their needs. Your baby will develop trust.

Babies who learn trust early in life have a healthy start that benefits them throughout their life. **You cannot *spoil* a baby**. Babies cry to let us know there is something that they need.

If by age 2 months your baby does not make eye contact with you, consult your child's health care provider.

"Play, smile and laugh with your baby.

"Babies go through the various stages of development at their own individual rates.

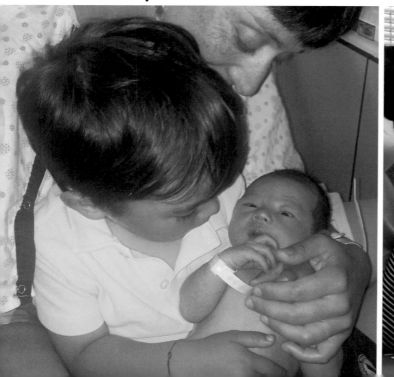

Development

Every baby is unique. Babies have their own personalities, right from the start. They go through the various stages of development at their own pace. For example, one baby might walk at 9 months, another not until 16 months. By 2 years of age, you can't tell which baby started earlier.

There are 'milestones' for development and what babies can usually do at different ages and stages.

It is helpful to know the stages of development, but it is most valuable to be physically and emotionally **present** with your baby. Look into your child's eyes. You can answer that text or email later. You will be building your child's healthy brain and your lifelong relationship.

Babies also learn from interactions with objects and pets in their environment, from sights and smells – in nature or in the house.

Children love cause-and-effect relations, like pressing on a buzzer and always hearing the sound. They can do that 20 times and not get bored.

Encourage your baby to explore all kinds of different objects, textures, and materials.

Visit the websites suggested in this book. You will find ways to support your child's development and guide their behaviours as they reach new milestones, including throwing food and toddler tantrums, both part of healthy development!

Talk to your health care provider or contact your Infant Development Program if you have any questions or concerns about your child's development.

"The best gift you can give your child is to be physically and emotionally present.

Emotions

E

Elephant

Babies learn to recognize emotions. They look to you to figure out whether a situation or an object is safe or not.

- learn to recognize how your baby is feeling
- learn to recognize how **you** are feeling
- respond to the cues your baby gives you to their feeling state
- name baby's feelings with words, even with young babies
- make use of times when you feel happy and positive to be with your baby
- take time out when you feel stressed, and do your best to become calm
- recognize when your baby is stressed or overstimulated
- make time to care for yourself

Practise mirroring your baby's feelings. This skill will be useful throughout your child's life, especially when they are a teenager!

"Your baby looks to you for how to act and feel.

"The nurture you give your child as a father adds to your child's development in unique and positive ways.

Fathering

FOX

Nurturing a baby is a shared
responsibility. Each parent contributes in
wonderful ways to the development of their baby.

During pregnancy, foster the connection
with your baby.

You can:

- learn what helps mothers and babies
- talk to your baby in the womb
- put your hand on your partner's belly and feel how your baby responds to your voice

Babies benefit when fathers hold them skin-to-skin
after birth and in the weeks following birth.
This is a powerful way to bond
with your baby.

Your nurture contributes to your child's wellbeing, future health, and physical and emotional growth.

- make time to hold, talk to and play with your baby every day
- care for your baby as much as you can – when dads feed or bathe baby, both dad and baby benefit
- read to your baby – fathers who read to their child improve their child's chances of learning to read and being happy and effective in school

Talk with those you trust about the changes a new baby brings to your life. Discuss ways to manage the stresses and responsibilities that come with the joys and opportunities of your new role.

Fathers who are the primary caregiver(s) can raise their children to be caring, productive, happy and healthy.

Grandfathers also play a special role, from holding babies skin-to-skin, to playing, storytelling and simply listening.

"Babies learn empathy from their caregivers.

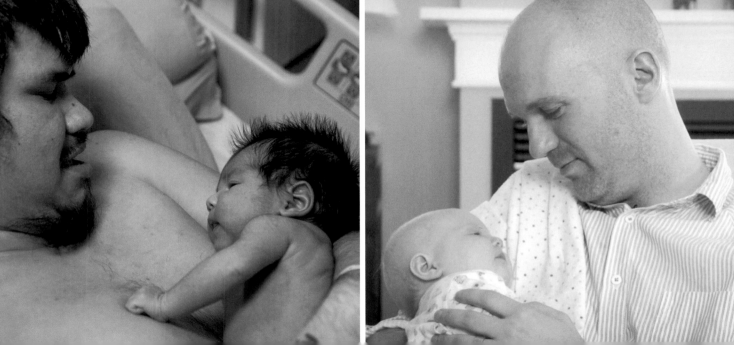

Give yourself a break

Parenting is hard work! It is important that you look after yourself. It is not humanly possible to care for another person 100% of the time.

Self-care means taking care of your health needs and doing something enjoyable every day. Walking is good for you and your baby. It builds a little activity into your day and gives you a break from the house.

Schedule time with your friends, partner, and family, or just by yourself. You cannot be your best if you are tired or stressed. And your baby needs "the best you."

"You are not alone.

Help - We all need it

Hen

Don't be shy to ask for help or delegate tasks. That way you can focus on caring for yourself and your baby. We all need help!

Be proactive and think about the help you will need **before your baby is born**. Talk to trusted friends or family members and let them know how they can best support you. When possible, create a list of people you can call on. Consider forming your own face-to-face or online parent group.

Traditionally, children were raised in a community. They still benefit when they know many people love and care about them.

Prenatal classes are a great way to build your support network. So are parent and baby groups. Talking to someone who is going through the same experiences can help you feel that you are not alone. For more information, call your local public health unit and see the resources at the back of this book.

" Immunizations are one of the best ways to prevent serious illness in childhood.

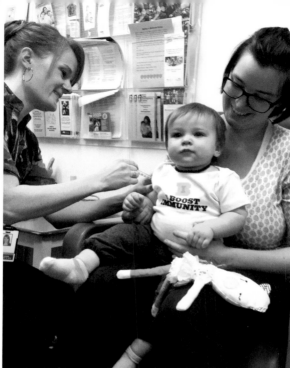

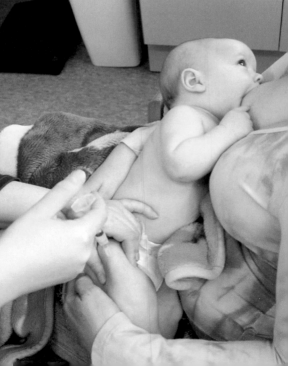

Immunizations

Iguana

When your baby needs immunizations or has a change in routine that might be upsetting, explain to your child how this will be helpful. Yes, even with a tiny baby!

Know that minor stresses, such as immunizations, help your child to develop resiliency, or coping skills.

It is important to immunize on time. You will protect your baby from many diseases and help prevent disease outbreaks in your community.

When the immunization is given:

- take a few deep breaths and relax – your child will be picking up on your feeling state
- capture your baby's interest with a favourite toy, bubbles or singing
- cuddle or breastfeed your baby, before, during and afterwards

Your soothing words will soon "repair" the situation.

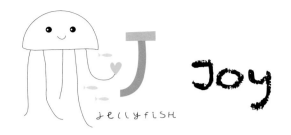

J Joy

Babies and toddlers are a source of great joy and fun. They enable us to be silly and laugh together. Children learn about the world around them, develop new skills and build resiliency through play.

- get down on the floor and PLAY with your baby or toddler
- have tummy time on the floor every day
- make funny faces
- talk and imitate your baby's sounds
- sing and sway to music
- read books together
- let your baby play with blocks and hold different things

Having fun together is one of the best ways to promote your child's social, emotional and physical development. This is the time to find your inner child.

"Having fun together is one of the best ways to promote your child's development.

"You are creating a deeper connection with your baby.

Kisses K

KANGAROO

It's hard to resist kissing babies,
and touch is so very important for
their development. As you kiss your baby's
toes and hands and belly, name the body parts.
Whether you are being tender or playful, you are
creating a deeper connection with your baby. Read
and respect your baby's cues and signals. Avoid
kissing your baby on the lips, especially if you
have a cold sore or are unwell. This will
prevent the spread of a virus and other
germs to your baby.

Language

Lion

Use whichever languages you are comfortable speaking. Your baby won't get confused and in fact, will benefit. Babies are language-learning machines! They are born ready to communicate and can easily manage more than one language. They have been learning about language since before they were born.

From the earliest possible moments, talk to your baby and watch for your baby's responses. This is called 'serve and return' or turn-taking.

- make up simple, even silly, songs and rhymes with your baby's name
- read to your baby using a sing-song voice
- tell stories – share your culture
- show pictures in a book (this book works well – babies love looking at babies!)

"Human interactions help children
understand the world.

MONKEY

Mothering

All babies need "mothering" from a special "somebody" who lovingly and consistently cares for them.

The research is clear – 'maternal warmth' helps babies overcome difficult circumstances, including illness or stress. Most often this comes from the baby's biological mother who may provide protective human milk through breastfeeding.

Other nurturing adults, such as fathers or adoptive parents, can wonderfully provide the "mothering" babies need to become socially and emotionally healthy. They can hold baby skin-to-skin, respond to baby's needs and become baby's special "somebody."

When a mother's own milk is not available, pasteurized donor human milk can be given to sick and very tiny babies.

"Mothering is central to a child's health and happiness.

"Nurture is the care and encouragement we give our babies to grow and develop.

Nurture

Narwhal

Early nurturing has a long-lasting impact on physical and mental health, and helps children learn to regulate or manage their emotions. It even helps them develop secure relationships throughout their lives!

It may take 3 months for your baby to smile back at you, but know that your love and nurturing will eventually be rewarded.

Nurture has a range of amazing impacts and yet it is made up of everyday actions.

- hold your baby skin-to-skin after birth and in the weeks following birth
- give healthy nourishment (breastfeed if you can)
- provide emotional warmth and physical safety
- touch your baby when giving daily care

Some other wonderful ways to nurture your baby are:

🧸 sing or hum

🧸 read and tell stories

🧸 turn-take (serve and return) when talking to baby

🧸 mirror baby's expressions and name the feelings

🧸 explain in a soothing voice what has happened,
is happening and will happen

🧸 read baby's cues and meet their physical and
emotional needs

🧸 share caregiving with the extended family and others
who are loving and trustworthy

Overstimulated O

OWL

Babies try to let parents know when they need a rest from a stimulating or busy activity. They:

- cry
- turn away
- sneeze
- yawn

They may need a few minutes of quiet or a nap. Babies who are well-rested from daytime naps (always using safe sleep recommendations) tend to sleep better at night.

Gradually, parents learn to read baby's cues. Sometimes parents worry when babies frown or cry. Often, baby is preparing for a big effort or simply tired.

Premature babies may get overstimulated more easily. Hold your baby skin-to-skin, use gentle strokes when massaging, and allow your baby more response time.

"Feeling safe is very important for brain and social-emotional development.

Predictability

P

Pig

Babies like to know what comes next. They do well with routines but don't need rigid schedules. Learning that you and the world around them are trustworthy and predictable is the foundation for healthy development. At all times, but particularly in times of stress, babies are comforted by familiar routines and familiar people. Knowing they can count on you to respond to their distress cries, to feed them when they're hungry, to change them when they are wet, and to put them to bed when they are tired, gives them a feeling of security. Create a predictable bedtime routine. Starting in the early days after birth, lay baby in their crib or safe sleep space, on their back, ideally while awake.

Q quail

Quiet Alert

Babies learn best in a quiet, alert state. As you get to know your baby, you will recognize when they are in that special receptive state of mind. Generally, babies are in a quiet alert state when they have slept, been fed, changed, and are calm. This is an ideal time to read to your baby, play and sing. Practise turn-taking as you talk with your baby. Or you may want to do all of these things while giving your baby a bath or a massage.

Relationship

A baby's first relationships shape ALL future relationships. That is why your baby's relationship with you is so very important. You may be surprised to know that the way you interact with your baby is **teaching** your baby how to interact with other people, even when they become an adult. At the same time you are building the lifelong relationship YOU will have with your child. Babies who have dependable and responsive caregivers over the early years of life learn trust and empathy. This protects babies and gives them confidence to explore their world and form and maintain healthy relationships with others.

Babies and young children often need to learn how to interact with other children. Parent-baby groups provide an ideal safe place for babies and young children to learn these skills with a parent there to guide them.

"Baby's first relationships shape ALL future relationships.

"You can protect your child by being calm and not sharing your stress.

Stress

S H E E P

Stresses are part of life and babies and children can cope with minor stresses. In fact, they need to experience them to learn resilience.

However, babies and young children are very vulnerable to ongoing, constant stress as this is toxic to their healthy development. Babies are aware, even when they are sleeping, of violence or other high levels of stress around them and need to be protected from it.

Try not to load your stress on your child. Instead, protect your child by working through the stress with trusted family, friends or professionals. When you do this you are teaching your child how to handle difficult situations.

If you are living in an unsafe environment, reach out to trusted family, friends or health professionals (see resources at the back of this book).

Touch

TIGER

Babies need to touch and be touched. Touch is necessary for healthy brain development and it is one of the senses through which babies can learn as soon as they are born.

- hold your baby skin-to-skin after birth and frequently during the following weeks and months
- cuddle your child throughout the early years, and beyond
- touch your baby as you feed them
- play games that involve touching and kissing your baby's skin
- help your baby discover the world through touch (and sight, hearing, smell and taste, as baby develops)

Let your baby take the lead. Respond to your baby's cues during massage and other touch. Babies let us know if they want a rest or more cuddles.

Remember, you will NOT spoil your baby by meeting their needs.

" Touch is essential for babies to thrive.

unicorn

Understanding

Babies can sense what is going on while still in the womb. Try to create a loving and low stress environment during pregnancy and after your child is born.

Even young babies understand pleasure and distress. They feel if something is safe or threatening. If babies feel frequently threatened, this can affect their healthy development.

Name feelings with words. In this way you teach your baby to make and regulate emotions and they will learn to do this by themself.

Nurturing babies is good for **every** baby's development.

" Babies experience feeling safe
or distressed long before they can speak.

"Babies around the world relax and feel safe when they hear a singsong voice.

Voice

V

Viper

Babies adore the sound of your voice.

During pregnancy, your baby hears your voice and begins to bond with you while still in the womb.

This is an ideal time to talk, sing and read to your baby.

Once baby is born, keep this up!

Singing is especially good. Babies love it when you sing, whether you think you are good at it or not.

Mothers, fathers, partners, other caregivers and even siblings, have a special way of talking to their baby. Often, they use a singsong voice, called "parentese" or "infant directed speech."

Babies around the world relax and feel safe when they hear this singsong voice. Research shows this contributes to their healthy brain development.

Talk to your baby as much as possible:

- use a comforting or singsong voice
- name how your baby is feeling
- show picture books and name what's in the pictures

Make up fun stories or tell stories about:

- yourself, your baby's family, or anything at all
- your traditions and heritage – as children grow and experience cultural events and foods, they will learn the meaning of your words

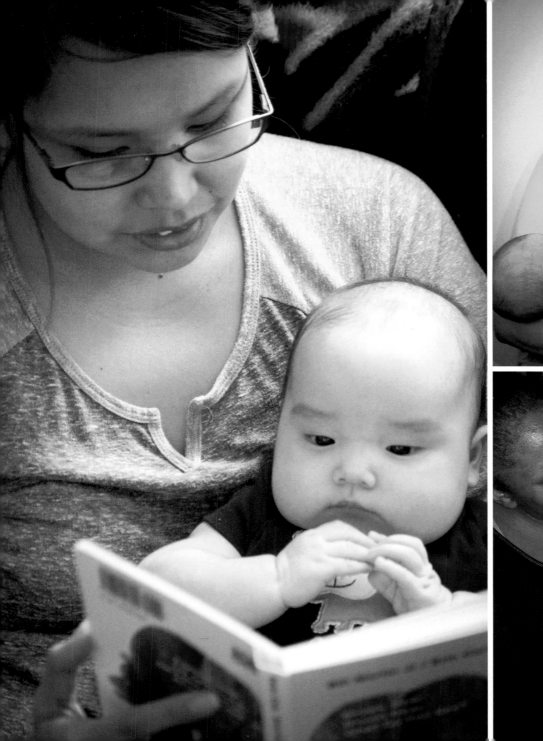

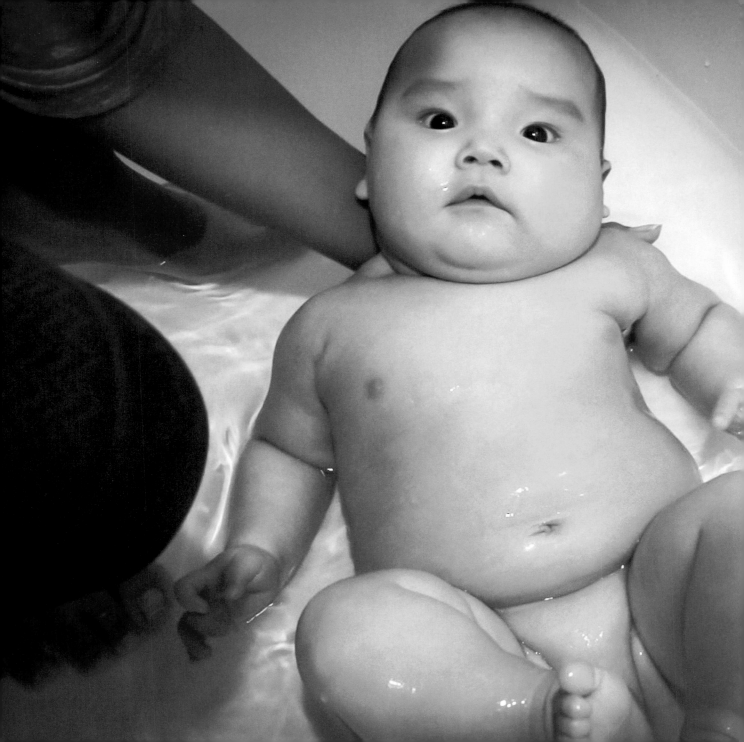

Water

W
WHALE

Parents are sometimes anxious about bathing a tiny baby, but babies find warm water familiar and soothing. Remember, your baby has spent 9 months floating in the womb. You will find everything you need to know about bathing babies in the four videos in the "Bathing baby" series. You will see how you can hold your baby securely in a warm bath so that your little one can relax and move their arms and legs.

X X-ray eyes

As a new parent, you might wish you had X-ray eyes to see what your baby is doing at every moment. Fortunately, babies don't need us to have superpowers.

Babies are happy to be left for short periods of time when they are in a safe place and feel fed, warm and secure. Make sure you can hear and respond to your baby's needs. Babies find a way to communicate to let us know when they need something.

Keep in mind, the definition of "a safe place" changes as your baby develops. However, it is never safe to leave baby alone at home, in the car, the bath, on an adult bed, a change table or couch.

"

You are
the most
important
person to
your baby.

You

Y Yak

Even while sleeping in your arms, your baby is aware of your presence. After all, your baby has known you and your voice since before birth. As the weeks and months go by, you and your baby will get to know each other better.

Nobody will know your baby as well as you.

Your baby needs your eye contact – put away your mobile device when interacting with your baby.

Try to keep your baby away from watching TV and other electronic screens for the first two years and then, only gradually introduce screen time. Remember, young children learn from interactions with people, animals, objects and their environment, not from screens.

Do not worry about trying to be perfect. Your baby does NOT need you to be perfect. Instead, be **present** with your baby.

Today's realities mean that we have busy lives and competing demands. You may have to temporarily put other things aside so that your baby comes first.

If you use child care, choose a provider who interacts warmly with children. Look for an appropriate and stimulating environment with age-appropriate toys and activities to support your child's growth and development.

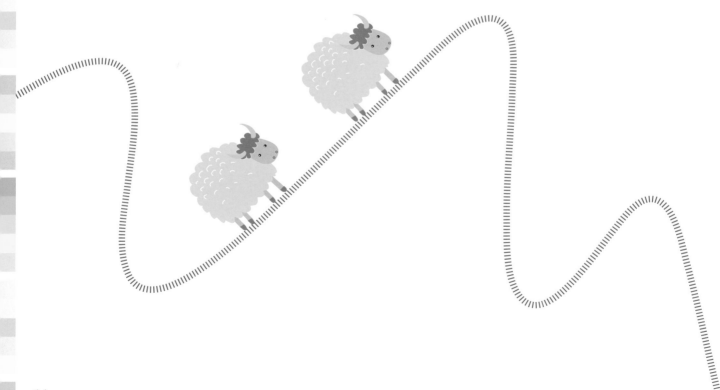

ZEBRA

ZZZsss

Lack of sleep may be the hardest challenge for parents. Aim to get at least 6 hours of sleep in a 24 hour period (easier said than done).

Everyone benefits when a parent is well-rested. Try to sleep when baby sleeps or call on trusted friends and family so you can catch up on sleep. The housework can wait!

You'll sleep better knowing that your baby is sleeping safely. Babies are safest sleeping on their back, on a firm mattress, in their own sleep space.

One day your child will sleep through the night. You may look back and wonder how you did so much while so sleep deprived. You may even miss this exceptional time in your life!

Resource List

KIDCARECANADA Society
www.kidcarecanada.org
Trustworthy videos and other resources for new parents and professionals that explain the importance of early nurture and show how to support social and emotional development in infants and toddlers. Many available in 11 languages.

HEALTHY FAMILIES BC websites:
www.healthyfamiliesbc.ca/parenting
BC Ministry of Health online platform for healthy living supports, tools and resources parents need for every age and stage of their child's development.

Baby's Best Chance: Parents' Handbook of Pregnancy and Baby Care
www.health.gov.bc.ca/library/publications/year/2017/BabysBestChance-Sept2017.pdf
This easy-to-read handbook gives parents trustworthy information based on best practices and evidence, to ensure a healthy pregnancy and baby.

Child Health Passport
www.healthyfamiliesbc.ca/about-us/additional-resources#CHP
BC Ministry of Health publications that support health professionals and families to raise healthy children.

Safe Sleep For My Baby
www.health.gov.bc.ca/library/publications/year/2017/safer-sleep-for-my-baby.pdf
Helping parents and caregivers create a safer sleep plan.

Toddler's First Steps

www.health.gov.bc.ca/library/publications/year/2017/ToddlersFirstSteps-Sept2017.pdf

Supports toddlers' optimal growth and development, aged 6–36 months.

Aboriginal Infant Development Program

www.aidp.bc.ca

Supports early identification of needs and early intervention for Indigenous children and families at risk.

Aboriginal Supported Child Development BC

www.ascdp.bc.ca

Recognizes the importance of cultural safety and early intervention. Supports the inclusion of Indigenous children with special needs in child-care and community settings.

Association of Neighbourhood Houses BC

www.anhbc.org

Provides programs and services for all ages, nationalities and abilities in a welcoming atmosphere.

Anxiety BC

www.anxietybc.com

A non-profit organization that promotes awareness of anxiety disorders and supports access to evidence-based resources and treatment.

BC Association of Family Resource Programs

www.frpbc.ca

A not-for-profit provincial organization. Promotes community-based Family Resource Programs (FRPs) where families access support and community resources.

BC Council for Families

www.bccf.ca

Celebrating the family's uniqueness. Dedicated to education programs and resources that help families grow stronger and even more resilient.

BC Mental Health Support Line

310-6789 (do not add 604, 778 or 250 before the number)

It's free and available 24 hours a day.

Best Start: Healthy Baby, Healthy Brain

www.healthybabyhealthybrain.ca/index.htm

Government of Ontario resource supporting service providers who implement health promotion programs for expectant and new parents, newborns and young children.

Canadian Pediatric Society

www.caringforkids.cps.ca/handouts/your_childs_development

Information for parents from Canada's paediatricians on the topic of what to expect as your child develops.

Canadian Red Cross

http://www.redcross.ca/training-and-certification/course-descriptions/first-aid-at-home-courses/emergency-child-care-first-aid---cpr

Describes the elements of emergency child care and first aid and lets you find courses available in your location.

Centre for Child Honouring

http://www.childhonouring.org/

Founded by Raffi, Child Honouring is a children-first approach to healing communities and restoring ecosystems.

Encyclopedia on Early Childhood Development

www.child-encyclopedia.com

Up-to-date scientific knowledge on early childhood development, from conception to age 5.

HealthLink BC

www.healthlinkbc.ca

Trusted health information is just a phone call or a click away. Quick and easy access to non-emergency health information and services at any time of the day or night. You can speak with a nurse, pharmacist, dietitian or other health professional to get advice, and find health services and resources near you.

Call 8-1-1 toll-free in B.C. or for deaf and hearing-impaired, call 7-1-1.

Heart–Mind Online

www.heartmindonline.org

Shares current research, scientific knowledge and best practices related to social and emotional development.

Here To Help

www.heretohelp.bc.ca/workbook/coping-with-depression-in-pregnancy-and-following-the-birth

A resource for women wanting to learn self-help skills to prevent and manage depression during pregnancy and after birth. Provides trustworthy mental health and substance abuse information.

Immunize BC

www.immunizebc.ca

BC Ministry of Health, the Centre for Disease Control and regional health authorities collaboration designed to improve the health of British Columbians.

The Infant Development Program
www.develop.bc.ca/programs/infant-development/
IDP promotes maximum development through evidence-based interventions, consultations, and education from birth to three years of age.

La Leche League Canada
www.lllc.ca/
Provides mother-to-mother breastfeeding support.

Parent-Child Mother Goose Programs
www.nationalpcmgp.ca/programs/listing/#BC
Provide a group experience for parents and their babies and young children. Focused on the pleasure and power of using rhymes, songs, and stories.

Pacific Post Partum Support Society
www.postpartum.org
Free or low-cost programs for mothers experiencing difficulty with adjustment, depression or anxiety.
Lower Mainland: 604.255.7999   Toll-free support: 1.855.255.7999

Perinatal Services BC
http://www.perinatalservicesbc.ca/
Provides leadership, support, and coordination for the strategic planning of perinatal services in British Columbia in collaboration with the Ministry of Health, health authorities and other key stakeholders.

Supported Child Development BC
www.bc-cfa.org/programs-services/supported-child-development/supported-child-development
Provides community-based services that enhance the quality of life for children, youth and adults with disabilities and their families.

VictimLinkBC

www2.gov.bc.ca/gov/content/justice/criminal-justice/victims-of-crime/victimlinkbc

A toll-free, confidential, multilingual telephone service available across BC and the Yukon 24 hours a day, 7 days a week at 1-800-563-0808. It provides information and referral services to all victims of crime and immediate crisis support to victims of family and sexual violence.

VROOM

www.joinvroom.org/?gclid=COLA8L7nv9ICFUJrfgodsr0LwQ

Using friendly and easy-to-understand language, and based on current research in neuroscience, VROOM shows parents and caregivers how they can make any of the moments they already share with their child brain-building moments.

Your Baby's Development: Age-Based Tips From Birth to 36 Months

www.zerotothree.org/resources/series/your-child-s-development-age-based-tips-from-birth-to-36-months#birth-to-12-months

Age-based handouts including "what to expect" charts for each age range.

Your Local Public Health Unit

www.immunizebc.ca/finder

This site helps families find the health unit closest to them.

Zero to Three: Early Connections Last a Lifetime (Parent Resources)

www.zerotothree.org/early-development/ages-and-stages

Resource List to help you learn about the skills and behaviours you can expect from your baby from birth to age 3.

Early Intervention

If you have engaged in the nurturing behaviours described in this ABC, and after several months your baby is still not responding as you would expect, **request a referral to an early intervention program from your health provider**. There are excellent programs for you and your baby and early intervention changes lives!

Trauma

If you have experienced **trauma**, some parts of parenting may be even more challenging for you. Trauma can interfere with your ability to be emotionally present for many reasons. It can:

- lead to problems in regulating your own emotions, so you may struggle with sometimes feeling too numb and other times feeling too overheated with emotions
- cause unhelpful beliefs about your ability to cope, and your safety in the world, especially in connecting to others
- create excessive feelings of guilt or shame that may take away from giving yourself permission to take care of your own needs and ask for help

If you notice that the effects of trauma are causing difficulties for you and your baby, speak to a health professional you trust.

—Dr. Joanna Cheek, MD, FRCPC, Assistant Clinical Professor, UBC Faculty of Medicine

Acknowledgements

This little book is the result of many collaborations between organizations and individuals. It represents the combined expertise of hundreds, even thousands, of years of experience from early childhood educators, health providers, researchers, parents and grandparents. They include – but are not limited to the individuals and organizations listed below:

Leadership Team
KIDCARECANADA Society
BC Ministry of Health
Vancouver Island Health Authority

KIDCARECANADA Society
Estelle Paget, Educator, Founder and Executive Director
Dr. Andrew Macnab, Pediatrician, Child Health Researcher
Elizabeth Wellburn, Instructional Designer
Sari Naworynski, Graphic Design
Alisa Kerr, HIDEF Productions Inc., Videos, Photos

BC Ministry of Health
Carolyn Solomon, Senior Manager, Maternal and Women's Health
Stacy White, Manager, Social/Emotional Health and Resiliency
Kelsey Ewart, Marketing Leader, Plain Language Expert
Keren Massey, Senior Policy Analyst, Early Childhood Health

Vancouver Island Health Authority
Dr. Dee Hoyano, Medical Health Officer
Helen Von Buchholz, Project Manager Public Health

Indigenous Reviewers and Contributors

Dr. Harjit Aulakh, Aboriginal Child and Youth Mental Health, Ministry of Children and Family Development
Diana Elliott, Provincial Advisor Aboriginal Infant Development Programs
Suzanne Jackson, Aboriginal Coordinator Success by Six
Francisca Waring, Aboriginal Supported Child Development Senior Consultant, Victoria Native Friendship Centre

Organizations

BC Council for Families • BC Healthy Child Development Alliance • Fraser Health Authority, Population and Public Health • Human Early Learning Partnership • Northern Health, Public Health • Peninsula Connections for Early Childhood • Vancouver Coastal Health, Public Health

Special thanks to the following contributors and reviewers:

Deb Baumann, Dana Brynelsen, Jennifer Cain, Catharine Campbell, Shelley Cardinal, Evie Chauncey, Dr. Joanna Cheek, Dr. Adele Diamond, Kimberly Dunlap, Dr. Lisa Feldman Barrett, Lea Geiger, Amy Ho, Stephanie Howell, Brenda Hurd, Dr. Padmapriya Kandhadai, Joel Kaplan, Dr. Christine Loock, Connie McKenzie, Karin Macaulay, Dr. Gabor Maté, Desiree Mercado, Vicki Neilson, Ruthild Ohl, Randi Parsons, Louise Parton, Ann Reiner, Pippa Rowcliffe, Dr. Kimberly Schonert-Reichl, Allison Smith, Dr. Carolyn Steinberg

Children's Hospital of Eastern Ontario (CHEO) MediaHouse and Public Health, Nanaimo BC for generously sharing their immunization photos

Lorna Crozier for giving us permission to use her books in our film shoots

KIDCARECANADA Board of Directors:

Carl Nilsen, Dr. Tisha Gangopadhyay, Kevin Koch, Mary Ann Cummings, Susan Evans, Sally Geller, Dr. Andrew Macnab, Heather McQueen, Estelle Paget

Index

About This Book

The messaging in this book aligns with current research and best practices in the areas of social and emotional development and public health. It is taken from our "Hugs for a Brighter Future" Educational Program. This educational program "translates" current research on early nurturing into accessible and appealing resources (over 100 videos) for parents, caregivers and health and educational professionals.

Quite naturally, most new parents focus on the practical aspects of caring for their new baby. They are often unaware of the importance of social and emotional health, now considered a key indicator of mental and emotional health and success in life. When more infants benefit from early nurturing, as described in this book and the resources, more children will grow to achieve their potential and become productive and compassionate members of society.

It is often said that "babies don't come with a manual." We hope this trustworthy little book provides guidance for families and professionals engaged in that most important role – raising the next generation.

We are indebted to the many contributors and reviewers who have shared their expertise.

–Estelle Paget, Executive Director, KIDCARECANADA Society